D0581903

THE BATHROOM SPORTS QUIZ BOOK

by

Jack Kreismer

RED-LETTER PRESS, INC.
Saddle River, New Jersey

ACKNOWLEDGMENTS

Project Development Coordinator:
Kobus Reyneke

Cover design and typography:
s.w.artz, inc.

Editorial:
Jeff Kreismer

Significant Others:
Theresa Adragna
Kathy Hoyt, Robin Kreismer
Jim & Rory Tomlinson, Lori Walsh

INTRODUCTION

For more than twenty years, the original Bathroom Library has entertained people on the go everywhere. With millions of copies out there, it proves that we're not all wet about bathroom reading.

Now, as heir to the throne, we proudly introduce a brand new Bathroom Library. We hope you enjoy this installment of it.

Yours flushingly,

Jack Kreismer
Publisher

THE
BATHROOM
SPORTS QUIZ
BOOK

*A Roll Call
of Challenging Trivia*

THE BATHROOM LIBRARY

RED-LETTER PRESS, INC.
Saddle River, New Jersey

FIRST OF ALL

1. Let's start the book with something as easy as ABC ... What do Herb Adderley, Kareem Abdul-Jabbar and Hank Aaron have in common?

2. What Kentucky Derby first did Favored Regret achieve in 1915?

3. What venue was the first site to host a World Series, a Super Bowl and an NCAA Final Four basketball tournament?

4. Who was baseball's first Rookie of the Year?

5. Who became the first golfer to earn $2 million in a season?

6. Joan Benoit won the initial running of what event in 1984?

7. Kenesaw Mountain Landis was the first to hold what job?

8. Who was the first play by play announcer for *Monday Night Football*?

9. What athletic shoemaker was first called Blue Ribbon Sports?

10. What is Magic Johnson's first name?

EXTRA POINT

"I'm not allowed to comment on lousy officiating."

-*Jim Finks*, New Orleans Saints G.M.

ANSWERS

1. Alphabetically, their names are listed first in each of their respective Halls of Fame: Adderley in the Pro Football Hall of Fame, Abdul-Jabbar in the Basketball Hall of Fame and Aaron in the Major League Baseball Hall of Fame.

2. Favored Regret was the first filly to win the famed horse race.

3. The Minnesota Metrodome, in a six month span from October, 1991 to March, 1992, accomplished all three.

4. Jackie Robinson, in 1947. (It wasn't until 1949 that the award was given to the top rookie in both the NL and AL.)

5. Tiger Woods, in 1997.

6. She won the first women's Olympic marathon.

7. Baseball commissioner … He served from 1920 to 1944.

8. Keith Jackson.

9. Nike.

10. Earvin.

EXTRA POINT

"There are forty-two golf courses in the Palm Springs area and nobody knows which one (Gerald) Ford is playing until after he hits his tee shot."

-*Bob Hope*, comedian

INITIALLY SPEAKING

In the quiz, the number on the left is based upon the first letters of each word provided on the right.

Example: 4 = Q. in a F.G. (Quarters in a Football Game)

1. 120 = Y. on a F. F. (I. the E.Z.)

2. 100 = P.S. by W.C. in one G.

3. 18 = H. on a G. C.

4. 48 = M. in a P. B. G.

5. 9-0 = S. of a F. B. G.

6. 10 = F. in B.

7. 3 = S. and Y. O.

8. 10 = F. in H. of a B. R.

9. 78 = F. in L. of a T. C.

10. 47 = M. L. of a B. M. (I. the M. B. R.)

EXTRA POINT

"I signed with the Milwaukee Braves for $3,000. That bothered my dad at the time because he didn't have that kind of dough. But he eventually scraped it up."

-**Bob Uecker**, broadcaster and former baseball player

ANSWERS

1. 120= Yards on a Football Field (Including the End Zones).

2. 100 = Points Scored by Wilt Chamberlain in one Game.

3. 18 = Holes on a Golf Course.

4. 48 = Minutes in a Pro Basketball Game.

5. 9-0 = Score of a Forfeited Baseball Game.

6. 10 = Frames in Bowling.

7. 3 = Strikes and You're Out.

8. 10 = Feet in Height of a Basketball Rim.

9. 78 = Feet in Length of a Tennis Court.

10. 47 = Maximum Length of a Boxing Match (Including the Minutes Between Rounds).

STADIA-MANIA

1. What two baseball stadiums have hosted the Olympics?

2. What current facility houses three professional teams simultaneously?

3. Do you know the two current pro football teams which played their home games in 1960, their inaugural year, in the Cotton Bowl?

4. Until 1988, this baseball stadium did not have lights. Name it.

5. What are the original names of the RCA Dome (Indianapolis), Edison International Field (Anaheim), and Pro Player Stadium (Miami)?

6. "Why does Texas Stadium have a hole in it?" is a popular joke about the home of the Dallas Cowboys. Do you know the answer?

7. Who's the only Yankee manager never to win a game in Yankee Stadium since they began play there?

8. Green Bay's football stadium was renamed Lambeau Field in 1965 following the death of the team's founder, Curly Lambeau. What was it first called?

9. Where is the U.S. Tennis Open played?

10. The Hall of Fame Game is played annually in Cooperstown at what field?

ANSWERS

1. Olympic Stadium in Montreal, in 1976, and Turner Field in Atlanta, in 1996.

2. Staples Center, home to the Lakers, Clippers and Kings.

3. The Dallas Cowboys and the Kansas City Chiefs. (The Chiefs were the Dallas Texans before they moved to K.C. in 1963.)

4. Wrigley Field.

5. The Hoosier Dome, Anaheim Stadium and Joe Robbie Stadium, respectively.

6. "So God can watch His favorite team."

7. Bill Virdon ... He managed the team in 1974-'75 when the Yanks played at Shea Stadium while Yankee Stadium was being renovated.

8. City Field.

9. Arthur Ashe Stadium.

10. Abner Doubleday Field.

JOIN THE CLUB

Match the team with its former name.

1. Tennessee Titans
2. Texas Rangers
3. New Jersey Devils
4. Sacramento Kings
5. Milwaukee Brewers
6. Chicago Bears
7. San Antonio Spurs
8. Baltimore Orioles
9. Colorado Avalanche
10. Washington Wizards

a) Seattle Pilots
b) Dallas Chaparrals
c) Quebec Nordiques
d) Decatur Staleys
e) Baltimore Bullets
f) Houston Oilers
g) Cincinnati Royals
h) Washington Senators
i) Colorado Rockies
j) St. Louis Browns

EXTRA POINT

"Never trust a baserunner with a limp. Comes a base hit and you'll think he just got back from Lourdes."

-*Joe Garagiola*, broadcaster and former baseball player

ANSWERS

1. F.

2. H.

3. I.

4. G.

5. A.

6. D.

7. B.

8. J.

9. C.

10. E.

EXTRA POINT

"I feel like I'm the best,
but you're not going to get me to say that."

-*Jerry Rice*, football wide receiver

HARDBALL TRIVIA

1. What's the only position not mentioned in Abbott and Costello's *Who's on First?* routine?

2. In 2002, Seattle Mariner teammates Mike Cameron and Brett Boone achieved something that had never been done in baseball. What?

3. The Cleveland Indians retired uniform number 455. Why?

4. What "first" do Sparky Anderson, Babe Ruth and Tom Seaver have in common?

5. Who was the youngest man elected to the Baseball Hall of Fame?

6. What three Chicago Cubs players were immortalized by the Franklin P. Adams poem, *Baseball's Sad Lexicon?*

7. What distinction does Masonori Murakami hold?

8. Do know the skipper who has managed more World Series victories (games) than any other?

9. These two baseball Hall of Famers once played for the Harlem Globetrotters. Pitch us their names.

10. Phillies great Mike Schmidt was voted starting NL third baseman for the 1989 All-Star Game, but didn't play. Why?

ANSWERS

1. Right field.

2. They became the first teammates to hit two back-to-back home runs in one inning. In addition, Cameron became the fifth player in big league history to hit four consecutive homers in one game.

3. It was done symbolically, to represent the number of consecutive sellouts from June 12, 1995 to April 2, 2001.

4. The same first name, George.

5. Sandy Koufax, 35, when elected in 1971.

6. Joe Tinker, Johnny Evers and Frank Chance - the famous "Tinker to Evers to Chance" double play combination. (During their time together from 1906 to 1909, they actually completed only 54 Dps.)

7. He was the first Japanese pitcher in major league history, with the San Francisco Giants in 1964 and '65.

8. Casey Stengel. His Yankee clubs won 37 games and lost 26. He piloted 10 World Series teams, winning seven.

9. Bob Gibson and Ferguson Jenkins.

10. He retired prior to the game.

FOUR-LETTER MEN

The answers to these question have last names which total four letters.

1. Who won the most batting titles in major league history?

2. Who is the NBA logo modeled after?

3. Can you name the NFL record holder for most interceptions in a season?

4. Who pitched for the Red Sox and Yankees, compiling a 94-46 won-loss record and a 2.28 lifetime ERA?

5. What tennis player was posthumously given the Presidential Medal of Freedom, America's highest civilian award, in 1993?

6. Who's the only NHL player to have two of his sons on the same team with him?

7. Of all the NFL quarterbacks whose last names begin with the letter Z, who has thrown the most touchdown passes?

8. His given name is Edson Arantes Do Nascimento. You know him better as whom?

9. Who said, "It doesn't matter whether you win or lose, it's how you play the game?"

10. See if this rings a bell: Who was the NFL's commissioner before Pete Rozelle?

ANSWERS

1. Ty Cobb, 12.

2. Jerry West.

3. Dick "Night Train" Lane, who intercepted 14 passes in 1952 for the Los Angeles Rams.

4. Babe Ruth.

5. Arthur Ashe.

6. Gordie Howe … His sons, Mark and Marty, skated with him on the 1979-'80 Hartford Whalers.

7. Jim Zorn, 111.

8. Soccer legend Pele.

9. Sportswriter Grantland Rice.

10. Bert Bell.

EXTRA POINT

"Sometimes, whether you're in the sixth grade or the eighth grade, you're going to make some shots to win the ball game and miss some shots to lose the ball game. Mine just happen to be on national TV."

-***Kobe Bryant***, basketball player

PHRASE CRAZE

See if you can figure out what sports phrases these items represent.

1. <u>COURT</u>
     2

2. H O M E

3. PLAY
     PLAY

4. EKORTS

5. DECI SION

6. OholeNE

7. <u>Mustard</u>
   Fastball

8. T
   O
   U
   C
   H

9. RETRAUQ

10. C   C
      H   H
        E
       C   C
     K   K

ANSWERS

1. Half court.

2. Home stretch.

3. Double play.

4. Backstroke.

5. Split Decision.

6. Hole in one.

7. Fastball with mustard on it.

8. Touchdown.

9. Quarterback.

10. Crosscheck.

EXTRA POINT

"We can't win at home. We can't win on the road. As general manager, I just can't figure out where else to play."

-*Pat Williams*, Orlando Magic G.M.

PLAYING BY THE RULES

1. How many technical fouls result in ejection from an NBA game?

2. In tennis, your serve goes wild and hits the recipient on the fly. Do you get credit for the point?

3. The first baseman trips and loses his glove. As he is lying on his stomach, he reaches out and makes the catch in his hat. Is this a legal catch?

4. A defensive player bats a forward pass up in the air. The quarterback catches his own pass. May he throw another forward pass?

5. What's the minimum number of players an NBA team must make available, meaning dressed in uniform and on the bench, for a game?

6. A field goal attempt grazes the helmet of the offensive right guard before it clears the uprights. Does the field goal count?

7. What's the maximum number of letters allowed for a race horse's name?

8. A line drive hits the pitcher's mound and ricochets into the first base dugout. Place the batter on the correct base.

9. When in-bounding a basketball, how much time do you have to release it?

10. In a bowling alley, how far apart must neighboring pins be?

ANSWERS

1. Two.

2. Yes.

3. No … It's a three base penalty for illegal use of equipment.

4. No.

5. Eight.

6. No.

7. 18.

8. It's a foul ball.

9. Five seconds.

10. Twelve inches.

EXTRA POINT

"If I had any imagination, I would have called myself Flip. Then there'd be Flip, Skip and Chip."

-*Harry Caray*, on his son and grandson who also became broadcasters

RUNNING NUMBERS

*Listed here are names of players who've had jerseys retired
by their respective clubs. What were their numbers?*

1. Carlton Fisk, Chicago White Sox

2. Floyd Little, Denver Broncos

3. Walt Frazier, New York Knicks

4. Bob Cousy, Boston Celtics

5. Eric Dickerson, St. Louis Rams

6. Bobby Clarke, Philadelphia Flyers

7. Robin Yount, Milwaukee Brewers

8. Ozzie Smith, St. Louis Cardinals

9. Jim Brown, Cleveland Browns

10. Mario Lemieux, Pittsburgh Penguins

EXTRA POINT

"If Casey Stengel were alive today,
he'd be spinning in his grave."

-*Ralph Kiner*, broadcaster and baseball Hall of Famer

ANSWERS

1. 72.

2. 44.

3. 10.

4. 14.

5. 29.

6. 16.

7. 19.

8. 1.

9. 32.

10. 66.

EXTRA POINT

"A lot of horses get distracted. It's just human nature."

*-**Nick Zito***, trainer of
1994 Kentucky Derby winner Go for Gin

SCREEN TEST

1. Milwaukee Bucks star Ray Allen played a much sought after high school sensation in this basketball flick. Do you know it?

2. *Major League* was a film about what bumbling big league team?

3. *Brian's Song* was a television movie about a Chicago Bears running back. What was Brian's last name?

4. What character did Robert Redford portray in the baseball film *The Natural*?

5. Can you name the 1999 film that purported to be a realistic look at pro football yet used all fictional teams because it wasn't sanctioned by the NFL?

6. *Fear Strikes Out* was a film about what zany baseball player of the '50s and '60s?

7. Broadway Joe Namath shared a bike and a romance with Ann-Margret in what 1970 movie?

8. Who starred in the golf flick *Happy Gilmore*?

9. The wife of Archibald Leach had a starring role in *Caddyshack II*. Can you name her? And, for extra credit, do you know her husband's stage name?

10. What football great starred in *The Dirty Dozen*?

ANSWERS

1. *He Got Game.*

2. The Cleveland Indians.

3. Piccolo.

4. Roy Hobbs.

5. *Any Given Sunday.*

6. Jimmy Piersall.

7. *CC and Company.*

8. Adam Sandler.

9. Dyan Cannon … Her husband was Cary Grant.

10. Jim Brown.

EXTRA POINT

"Men forget everything; women remember everything.
That's why men need instant replay in sports.
They've already forgotten what happened."

-***Rita Rudner***, comedienne

LEFT-HANDED COMPLIMENTS

1. Can you name the coach of Maryland University's basketball team through the '70s and mid-'80s?

2. What southpaw pitched his franchise's first-ever regular-season perfect game on May 17, 1998?

3. This Hall of Famer pitched for Connie Mack's Athletics from 1925 to 1933, and for the Red Sox from 1934 to 1941. His career record was 300-141. Do you know him?

4. Which left-handed tennis player retired as the all-time leader among men and women in singles titles with 167?

5. *You Cannot Be Serious* is the autobiography of what tennis great?

6. What lefty basketballer is known as The Admiral?

7. Name the center who was on 11 championship NBA teams and later became player-coach of the club.

8. He was National League MVP in 1992 with one team and in 1993 with another club.

9. Who has the most career no-hitters as a lefthander?

10. What lefty was the NFL's number one draft pick in 2001?

ANSWERS

1. Lefty Driessell.

2. David Wells of the New York Yankees.

3. Lefty Grove.

4. Martina Navratilova.

5. John McEnroe.

6. David Robinson.

7. Bill Russell.

8. Barry Bonds, with the Pirates and Giants.

9. Sandy Koufax, four.

10. Michael Vick.

EXTRA POINT

"I led the league in 'Go get 'em next time.'"

-*Bob Uecker*, broadcaster and former baseball player

GRIDIRON GAMES

1. With what team did former Bills quarterback Jim Kelly make his professional debut?

2. In what city did the San Diego Chargers play in 1960, their first year of existence?

3. Before the Rams played in St. Louis, they played in Anaheim, California. Prior to that, they played in Los Angeles. Where did they play before that?

4. Which two college football teams vie for the Little Brown Jug?

5. Who's the only two-time Heisman Trophy winner?

6. This former player was the first draft choice in USFL history but never played a down in that league opting, instead, to play in the NFL. Name him.

7. The first team name to be retired in NFL history occurred in 1998. What team?

8. What was the Super Bowl formerly called?

9. Who manufactures NFL footballs?

10. Who's been sacked more times than anyone in NFL history?

ANSWERS

1. The Houston Gamblers of the USFL.

2. Los Angeles.

3. Cleveland.

4. Michigan and Minnesota.

5. Archie Griffin, of Ohio State.

6. Dan Marino.

7. The Oilers ... When the Tennessee Oilers (nee Houston) decided to change their name to the Titans, the NFL decided to retire the former name.

8. The AFL-NFL Championship Game.

9. Wilson.

10. John Elway.

EXTRA POINT

"Joe who did you say? Oh, Frazier. Yeah, I remember him. He's the one who leads with his face all the time."

-Muhammad Ali

FACT OR FIB?

1. Baseball's "doubleheader" was borrowed from the soccer term "header." In days gone by, when a twinbill was played on English soccer fields it was referred to as a doubleheader.

2. The Harlem Globetrotters, founded in 1926, didn't play a game in Harlem until 1969.

3. Hank Aaron holds the Milwaukee Braves career home run record.

4. Wilt Chamberlain never fouled out of an NBA game.

5. Carl Lewis was the first athlete to win gold medals in the same event in four consecutive Olympics.

6. Former First Lady Hillary Clinton is an honorary member of the LPGA Hall of Fame.

7. Polo was never played at the Polo Grounds (former home of baseball's New York Giants and Mets).

8. Rocky Marciano is boxing's only undefeated heavyweight champ.

9. The area between miles 16 and 18 of the Boston Marathon is called the Beantown Massacre.

10. Upset was the name of the only horse to defeat racing great Man O' War.

ANSWERS

1. Fib … It derived from railroad jargon. Doubleheader is lingo for a train with two engines.

2. Fact … Originating in Chicago as the "Savoy Five," the hoopsters played some 9,500 games before appearing in Harlem.

3. Fib … Eddie Mathews, with 452 of his 512 homers as a Milwaukee Brave, holds the record. Of Aaron's 755 roundtrippers, 398 were hit while with the Braves.

4. Fact … And the Stilt played in 1,045 contests.

5. Fib … Al Oerter was the first, winning gold medals in the discus throw in every Olympics from 1956 through 1968.

6. Fib … But another former First Lady is - Betty Ford.

7. Fact.

8. Fact.

9. Fib … It's called Heartbreak Hill.

10. Fact.

EXTRA POINT

"No, I never broke my nose playing ice hockey; but eleven others did."

-*Gordie Howe*, hockey Hall of Famer

GIRL TALK

1. Venus and Serena Williams were ranked number one and number two in the world when they played each other in the French Open and Wimbledon in 2002. Who won?

2. Name the '90s baseball flick which starred Rosie O'Donnell and Madonna.

3. Who was the first woman to drive in the Indianapolis 500?

4. Do you know the first woman to be named Athlete of the Year by *Sports Illustrated*? (Hint: The year was 1972.)

5. What Olympic gymnast later played Peter Pan on TV and on stage?

6. What "sweet sixteen" defeated Steffi Graf for the tennis gold medal at the 1992 Barcelona Olympics?

7. Who was the first African-American player to win Wimbledon?

8. What female won Final Four basketball MVP honors in both 1983 and '84? (Hint: She's currently an NBA broadcaster.)

9. What was the real first name of all around athlete Babe Didrikson Zaharias?

10. Who won golf's 2000 Nabisco Championship and celebrated by jumping into the lake near the 18th hole?

ANSWERS

1. Serena, both times.

2. *A League of Their Own.*

3. Janet Guthrie.

4. Billie Jean King.

5. Cathy Rigby.

6. Jennifer Capriati.

7. Althea Gibson.

8. Cheryl Miller.

9. Mildred.

10. Karrie Webb.

EXTRA POINT

"I find that prayers work best when you have big players."

-***Knute Rockne***, Notre Dame football coach

CHIP SHOTS

1. Has Tiger Woods won every Major?

2. At what golfer's house was President Clinton when he fell down the steps and injured his knee in 1997?

3. How old do you have to be to play on the Senior PGA tour?

4. What trophy is awarded to the golfer maintaining the lowest scoring average in PGA events?

5. At 5'4" tall, he's the shortest winner of the Masters. Name him.

6. Who holds the record for the longest time between victories at the Masters?

7. What movie was filmed at the Rolling Hills Golf Resort in Ft. Lauderdale, Florida?

8. Harold Stilson became the oldest golfer to make a hole in one, at a country club in Deerfield Beach, Florida on May 16, 2001. Give or take a year, how old was he?

9. Who was known as Champagne Tony?

10. Born Leslie King Jr., he's a golf-loving former U.S. president. Do you know him?

EXTRA POINT

"If you can't be an athlete, at least be an athletic supporter."

-Eve Arden

ANSWERS

1. Yes.

2. Greg Norman's.

3. 50.

4. The Vardon Trophy.

5. Ian Woosnam.

6. Jack Nicklaus … He first won the tournament in 1963 and then again in 1986, a span of 23 years.

7. *Caddyshack*.

8. 101.

9. Tony Lema.

10. Gerald Ford.

EXTRA POINT

"My wife made me a millionaire -
I used to have three million."

-***Bobby Hull***, hockey Hall of Famer, on his divorce

MISCELLANEOUS MINDBENDERS

1. Who was elected to baseball's Hall of Fame with the highest percentage of votes?

2. With what league are the Saskatchewan Roughriders, Hamilton Tiger-Cats and Calgary Stampeders associated?

3. Who was the first player to unanimously win the NHL's Hart Trophy as most valuable player?

4. Who is the shortest player in NBA history?

5. Can a pitcher's baseball glove be green?

6. Affirmed is horse racing's last Triple Crown winner. Can you name its jockey?

7. What innovation of the American Basketball Association remained after the merger with the NBA?

8. Who's the only man to win tennis' Grand Slam twice?

9. What's the name of the emblem on the New Orleans Saints helmet?

10. What hoopster led the NBA, ABA and NCAA in scoring and had two sons play in the NBA?

ANSWERS

1. Tom Seaver.

2. The Canadian Football League.

3. Wayne Gretzky, in 1981-'82.

4. 5'3" Tyrone "Muggsy" Bogues.

5. Yes ... It may be any solid color except white or grey.

6. Steve Cauthen.

7. The three-point basket.

8. Rod Laver.

9. It's called a *fleur de lis.*

10. Rick Barry.

EXTRA POINT

"Who needs the NFL with all of their stupid rules like "no taunting"? You can hit a guy at full speed and put him in the hospital but you can't say 'Nah nah! Quarterback has a big butt!'"

-***Drew Carrey***, comedian

PRIZE PACKAGES

1. What Heisman Trophy winner later went on to an NBA career?

2. What sports owner was named *Time*'s Man of the Year in 1991?

3. What cup do U.S. and European golf teams vie for biennially?

4. What award is given to the NBA champion?

5. Who has won golf's green jacket the most?

6. Which horse was not a Triple Crown winner: Secretariat, Seattle Slew or War Emblem?

7. What "prized" title is given to the last man selected in the NFL draft?

8. In soccer, what was the World Cup Trophy previously called?

9. Does the NHL championship team get to keep the Stanley Cup?

10. Who gets the Borg-Warner Trophy?

Extra Point

"Alright everyone, line up alphabetically according to your height."

-Casey Stengel

ANSWERS

1. Charlie Ward.

2. Ted Turner, owner of the Atlanta Braves.

3. The Ryder Cup.

4. The Larry O'Brien Trophy.

5. Jack Nicklaus, six times.

6. War Emblem.

7. Mr. Irrelevant.

8. The Jules Rimet Cup.

9. No … It's on loan to them for one year.

10. The winner of the Indianapolis 500.

SECOND GUESSING

1. Pro football's winningest coach in history is Don Shula with a total of 347 victories. Who's second?

2. Tom Dempsey kicked an NFL record 63-yard field goal in 1970. Who was second to do that?

3. Roger Bannister was the first to run a mile under four minutes, in 1954. Who was the second miler to do so?

4. Pete Rose has had more big league at bats, 14,053, than anyone else. Who's second?

5. UCLA has the most NCAA Divison I basketball titles, 11. Who's second?

6. With 9 Olympic gold medals, Mark Spitz has won more than anyone. Who is second with eight?

7. Among male golfers, Jack Nicklaus has the most Major tournament wins, 18. Who's second?

8. Even though he hit .406 in 1941 (and is baseball's last .400 hitter), Ted Williams finished second in the A.L. MVP voting to what player?

9. The San Francisco 49ers and Dallas Cowboys are tied with the most Super Bowl wins, 5. Which team is second with 4?

10. Who's second on baseball's all-time home run list?

ANSWERS

1. George Halas, 324.

2. Jason Elam, in 1998.

3. John Landy.

4. Hank Aaron, 12,364.

5. Kentucky, 9.

6. Matt Biondi.

7. Walter Hagen, 11.

8. Joe DiMaggio.

9. The Pittsburgh Steelers.

10. Babe Ruth, with 714 homers.

EXTRA POINT

"Every year Tommy offers $50,000 to the family
of the unknown soldier."

-**Don Sutton**, on manager Tommy Lasorda's frugal ways

A MAN FOR ALL SEASONS

Name the all around athlete from the clue given.

1. A Hall of Fame running back who scored the most points in an NFL game, he was also a pitcher for the St. Louis Browns.

2. In the '90s he played for two teams in the same city, the Braves and Falcons.

3. Who won a championship with baseball's Milwaukee Braves in 1957 and titles with the 1959, '60 and '61 Boston Celtics?

4. He was a major league first baseman and played in a Super Bowl for the Packers as a defensive back. Name him.

5. What Olympic bobsledder played for the USFL's Generals and, in the NFL, for the Cowboys, Vikings and Giants to name a few?

6. The most famous athlete of his time, this man joined the Canton Bulldogs football team in 1915, was an Olympic gold medalist and a major league baseball player. Who is he?

7. Who played on baseball's Royals, White Sox and Angels and was a Raiders running back from 1987-'90?

8. Who's the only man to coach a team (the Vikings) in the Super Bowl and to play on an NBA championship team (the 1950 Minneapolis Lakers) ?

9. Who played parts of three seasons with baseball's Blue Jays but had more success with basketball's Celtics? (Hint: He later became an NBA coach.)

10. An All-America basketball star at Duke who played briefly for the NBA Pistons, he moved on to baseball and won the NL MVP while on the 1960 World Champion Pirates. Name him.

ANSWERS

1. Ernie Nevers.

2. Deion Sanders.

3. Gene Conley.

4. Tom Brown.

5. Herschel Walker.

6. Jim Thorpe.

7. Bo Jackson.

8. Bud Grant.

9. Danny Ainge.

10. Dick Groat.

EXTRA POINT

"McCovey swings and misses, and it's fouled back."

-*Jerry Coleman*, Padres announcer

JOCK ROCK

The following crowd-pumping tunes are heard
in arenas and stadiums throughout the land.
See if you can put them in harmony with the recording artist.

1. *YMCA*

2. *Na, Na, Hey, Hey,*
   Kiss Him Goodbye

3. *Who Let the Dogs Out*

4. *Tubthumping*

5. *The Monday Night Football*
   Theme Song

6. *Can U Feel It*

7. *We Will Rock You*

8. *Get Down Tonight*

9. *Whoomp! There It Is*

10. *Shout*

a) K.C. and the Sunshine Band

b) Queen

c) The Isley Brothers

d) The Village People

e) Baja Men

f) Chumbawamba

g) Steam

h) 3rd Party

i) The team

j) Hank Williams Jr.

EXTRA POINT

"I am the best tennis player who cannot play tennis."

-Ian Tiriac, pro tennis coach

ANSWERS

1. D.

2. G.

3. E.

4. F.

5. J.

6. H.

7. B.

8. A.

9. I.

10. C.

EXTRA POINT

"If I drop dead tomorrow,
at least I'll know I died in good health."

-*Bum Phillips*, football coach, after passing his physical

HOOP SCOOP

1. The L.A. Lakers swept the N.J. Nets in 2002 for a three-peat. Has any NBA team won more than three championships in a row?

2. Do you know the player who was nicknamed "The Big E" and played exactly 50,000 minutes in his NBA career?

3. Who is the Red Auerbach Trophy given to?

4. What was the last college basketball team to win back-to-back NCAA tournament titles?

5. Who is the NBA's all-time winningest coach?

6. UCLA holds the record for most consecutive basketball victories. How many?

7. With what minor league team did Michael Jordan attempt a baseball career?

8. Alright, baby boomers: Jerry West was the second player taken in the 1960 NBA draft. Who was first? (Hint: Think "Big.")

9. Name the first African-American head coach to win an NCAA title.

10. With what team did Julius Erving begin his professional basketball career?

ANSWERS

1. Yes … The Boston Celtics won eight straight titles, from 1958-'59 to 1965-'66.

2. Elvin Hayes.

3. The NBA coach of the year.

4. Duke, in 1991 and 1992.

5. Lenny Wilkens.

6. 88.

7. Birmingham Barons.

8. The Big O - Oscar Robertson.

9. John Thompson, Georgetown.

10. The Virginia Squires of the ABA.

EXTRA POINT

"No ma'am, I'm a jockey for a dinosaur."

-*Johnny Kerr*, when asked if he played basketball

LAUGH-IN TIME-OUT

It's time to enjoy (and we use that term loosely)
a break with some "jock"ularity.

1. When do bowling pins lie down?

2. Where did they put the matador who joined the baseball club?

3. What do you get if you cross a bowling lane with a famous heavyweight boxer?

4. Why was Japanese ice hockey a failure at the box office?

5. How does Michael Jordan change a light bulb?

6. What do you get when you cross a hen with a bookmaker?

7. What's the only creature that can take thousands of people for a ride at the same time?

8. What do you get when you cross a fighter with a telephone?

9. How does Brett Favre change a light bulb?

10. How many college basketball players does it take to screw in a light bulb?

ANSWERS

1. When they go on strike.

2. In the bullpen.

3. Muhammad Alley.

4. No one had a yen for it.

5. He fakes it out of its socket.

6. A chicken that lays odds.

7. A racehorse.

8. A boxing ring.

9. He passes the job to a receiver.

10. One … but he gets three credits for it.

WHO AM I?

1. I am the only boxer to defeat Mike Tyson twice.

2. I scored the first touchdown in Super Bowl history.

3. In 1984, I was drafted by the NHL's Los Angeles Kings but wound up on another playing field with the Atlanta Braves.

4. I'm an LPGA Hall of Famer married to baseballer Ray Knight.

5. There's a 15-foot-tall statue of me outside the Northlands Coliseum, hoisting the Stanley Cup over my head.

6. I hold the big league record for grand slams in a season, 6.

7. I am the shortest player to win an NBA scoring title.

8. I set a Super Bowl passing record with 414 yards.

9. In 1998, at the age of 62, I became the oldest player to survive the 36-hole cut at the Masters.

10. I am the last man from Army to win the Heisman Trophy.

EXTRA POINT

"Skiing combines outdoor fun
with knocking down trees with your face."

-**Dave Barry**, humorist

ANSWERS

1. Evander Holyfield.

2. Max McGee.

3. Tom Glavine.

4. Nancy Lopez.

5. Wayne Gretzky.

6. Don Mattingly.

7. The Answer (pun intended) - 6' Allen Iverson.

8. Kurt Warner.

9. Gary Player.

10. Pete Dawkins, in 1958.

EXTRA POINT

"If it's undisputed, what's all the fighting about?"

-*George Carlin*, comedian, referring to
the boxing term "undisputed champion"

BY ANY OTHER NAME

Each of the following is not generally known by his given name. Identify him by the clues given.

1. Oail (yes, Oail) always wore a hat on the sidelines unless he was coaching in a domed stadium.

2. Eldrick was the youngest Masters winner ever.

3. Norman was fired by ABC after two seasons in the booth on *Monday Night Football.*

4. Harold gave professional football instant credibility when he joined the Bears in 1925.

5. Wilbur was the only head coach to win an AFL and an NFL championship.

6. Leroy is a Hall of Fame pitcher with a "lifetime" record of 28-31. His best work, however, came in the Negro Leagues.

7. Charles was Chuck Noll's very first draft choice with the Pittsburgh Steelers.

8. Anthony was AL Rookie of the Year with the Red Sox in 1997.

9. Another Anthony, despite being just 5' 7", won an NBA slam dunk contest.

10. Johnnie is often credited with popularizing the "high five" with the '70s Dodgers.

ANSWERS

1. Bum Phillips.

2. Tiger Woods.

3. Boomer Esiason.

4. Red Grange.

5. Weeb Ewbank.

6. Satchel Paige.

7. Joe Greene.

8. Nomar Garciaparra.

9. Spud Webb.

10. Dusty Baker.

EXTRA POINT

"He who lives by the cheap shot, dies by the cross-check."

-*Stan Fischler*, broadcaster and hockey historian

AUTO-MOTIVES

The answers to each of these questions contain the make or model of an automobile (past or present).

1. What do Alan Page, Pat Summerall, Lynn Swann and Drew Pearson have in common?

2. Name the site which hosted a Super Bowl and has been home to an NBA and NFL team.

3. Name the baseball commissioner who put an asterisk after Roger Maris' 61 homers because he'd achieved it in a 162 game schedule rather than the 154 game season when Babe Ruth hit 60 in 1927.

4. With what team did Johnny Unitas wind up his career?

5. Memorial Stadium, home of college football's Cornhuskers, is located where?

6. With a World Series pitching record of 10-8, he's both won and lost the most games in the Fall Classic. And his name is...?

7. They won back-to-back Super Bowls in '98 and '99.

8. Larry Csonka and another running back made the 1972 Dolphins the first team in NFL history to have two 1,000 yard rushers. Do you know him?

9. Who plays their home games in the Georgia Dome?

10. What player made the NBA's first three-point shot (in the 1979-'80 season)?

ANSWERS

1. They all wore number 88 (as in the Oldsmobile 88).

2. The Pontiac Silverdome.

3. Ford Frick.

4. The San Diego Chargers.

5. Lincoln, Nebraska.

6. Whitey Ford.

7. The Broncos (as in the S.U.V.)

8. Mercury Morris.

9. The Falcons (as in the extinct vehicle).

10. Chris Ford.

EXTRA POINT

"I've just played World War Two golf -
out in 39 and back in 45."

-*Lee Trevino*, golfer

HALLS OF FAME

Match the Hall of Fame with the city in which it's located.

1. Hockey
2. Tennis
3. Skiing
4. Bowling
5. Swimming
6. Basketball
7. Golf
8. Football
9. Baseball
10. Figure Skating

a) Springfield, MA
b) Colorado Springs, CO
c) Cooperstown, NY
d) Canton, OH
e) Toronto, Ontario
f) Pinehurst, NC
g) Vail, CO
h) Newport, RI
i) St. Louis, MO
j) Ft. Lauderdale, FL

EXTRA POINT

"Fear was absolutely necessary.
Without it, I would have been scared to death."

-*Floyd Patterson*, former heavyweight boxing champ

ANSWERS

1. E.

2. H.

3. G.

4. I.

5. J.

6. A.

7. F.

8. D.

9. C.

10. B.

EXTRA POINT

"Anthony's only negative is that he has no negatives."

-Jim McNally, line coach,
on Bengals lineman Anthony Munoz

THAT WAS THE YEAR THAT WAS

Give the year for each of the following headlines.

1. SPITZ CAPTURES 7 GOLD MEDALS

2. MARINO ANNOUNCES RETIREMENT

3. JENNER TAKES DECATHLON

4. AFFIRMED WINS TRIPLE CROWN

5. GREEN BAY TAKES FIRST SUPER BOWL

6. U.S. WINS WOMEN'S WORLD CUP

7. GORDON NAMED NASCAR ROOKIE OF THE YEAR

8. CLAY BEATS LISTON

9. RUTH HITS 60

10. BULLS THREE-PEAT 2ND TIME IN DECADE

EXTRA POINT

"I just try to concentrate on concentrating."

*-**Martina Navratilova**, tennis player*

ANSWERS

1. 1972.

2. 2000.

3. 1976.

4. 1978.

5. 1967.

6. 1999.

7. 1993.

8. 1964.

9. 1927.

10. 1998.

WHO SAID IT?

1. "The average attendance at Cubs games this year is 48 degrees."
   a) Harry Caray b) Mark Grace c) Ernie Banks d) Tyra Banks

2. "I know I'm getting better at golf, because I'm hitting fewer spectators." a) Chi Chi Rodriguez b) Gerald Ford
   c) Raymond Floyd d) Pink Floyd

3. "I'm leading the league in technicals. Better to be silent and be a fool than to open your mouth and remove all doubt."
   a) Dennis Rodman b) Charles Barkley c) Rasheed Wallace
   d) Mike Wallace

4. "In 1962, I was voted Minor League Player of the Year. Unfortunately, that was my second year in the majors."
   a) Bob Uecker b) Jimmy Piersall c) Nellie Fox d) Silent Fox

5. "We're experiencing audio technicalities." a) Ralph Kiner
   b) Bob Costas c) Jerry Coleman d) Gary Coleman

6. "The NFL, like life, is full of idiots." a) Jerry Glanville
   b) Mike Ditka c) Randy Cross d) Christopher Cross

7. "Jerry Rice is the greatest and I'm the best." a) Andre Rison
   b) Randy Moss c) Keyshawn Johnson d) Don Johnson

8. "We have deep depth." a) Yogi Berra b) Andy Van Slyke
   c) Dizzy Dean d) Jimmy Dean

9. "Lots of people look up to Charles Barkley. That's because he's just knocked them down." a) Chuck Daly b) Pat Riley
   c) Phil Jackson d) Jessie Jackson

10. "If you slid into bases head first for twenty years, you'd be ugly, too." a) George Brett b) Rickey Henderson
    c) Pete Rose d) Tokyo Rose

ANSWERS

1. A.

2. B.

3. B.

4. A.

5. A.

6. C.

7. A.

8. A.

9. A.

10. C.

EXTRA POINT

"My greatest strength is that I have no weaknesses."

-*John McEnroe*, tennis player

THE ONE AND ONLY

1. Who's the only player in NBA history to win the MVP Award, the Defensive Player of the Year Award and the MVP Award for the NBA Finals? (Hint: The year was 1994.)

2. Who's the only quarterback to play in five Super Bowls?

3. In 1985 who became the only unseeded tennis player to win the Wimbledon singles title?

4. How about identifying the only golfer to hold all four Grand Slam titles at once?

5. Who's the only three-time American Basketball Association MVP winner? (Hint: He's also the only ABA and NBA MVP winner.)

6. Who's the only jockey to win two Triple Crowns? (Hint: He did it with Whirlaway in 1941 and with Citation in 1948.)

7. Name the only man to captain two franchises to Stanley Cup victories.

8. What pitcher started 16 Opening Day Major League games?

9. Who's the only fighter to knock out Muhammad Ali in a heavyweight championship bout?

10. What's the only Super Bowl team to go undefeated during the regular season?

ANSWERS

1. Hakeem Olajuwon.

2. John Elway.

3. Boris Becker.

4. Tiger Woods.

5. Julius Erving.

6. Eddie Arcaro.

7. Mark Messier, the Oilers and the Rangers.

8. Tom Seaver.

9. Larry Holmes (by an 11th round TKO).

10. The 1972 Miami Dolphins.

EXTRA POINT

"I went fishing the other day with a dotted line.
I caught every other fish."

-*Steven Wright*, comedian

MONOGRAMMED MEN

Identify the man from the initials and clues.

1. M.O. - One of the Rams "Fearsome Foursome," he starred in the TV series *Father Murphy*.

2. H.R. - Shocked Lennox Lewis to win the WBC/IBF heavyweight championship.

3. L.A. - Soared to greatness at the Tour de France.

4. B.W. - He led the NFL in rushing in its first two seasons and later was on the bench, appointed to the U.S. Supreme Court in 1962.

5. D.E. - Sr. and Jr., there's a race to answer this one.

6. T.B. - Had a Super day February 3, 2002.

7. J.R. - Was the first high schooler to run the mile in under four minutes.

8. J.D. - St. Louis outfielder who goes by his initials.

9. L.B. - The "hick from French Lick."

10. J.N. - The doctor who had the right prescription for basketball.

ANSWERS

1. Merlin Olsen.

2. Hasim Rahman.

3. Lance Armstrong.

4. Byron "Whizzer" White.

5. Dale Earnhardt.

6. Tom Brady.

7. Jim Ryun.

8. J.D. Drew ... To confound matters his name is actually David Jonathan Drew, so does that mean he should be a DJ?

9. Larry Bird.

10. Dr. James Naismith, the inventor of the game.

EXTRA POINT

"We'll do all right if we can capitalize on our mistakes."

*-**Mickey Rivers***, baseball player

AUTHOR! AUTHOR!

Who penned the following books?

1. *Hey! Wait a Minute! I Wrote a Book!*
   a) John Madden b) Casey Stengel c) Jackie Robinson
   d) Mrs. Robinson

2. *Ball Four*
   a) Warren Spahn b) Jim Bouton c) Robin Roberts
   d) Julia Roberts

3. *Paper Lion*
   a) Barry Sanders b) George Plimpton c) Night Train Lane
   d) Lois Lane

4. *Just Give Me the Damn Ball*
   a) Bob Gibson b) Charles Barkley c) Keyshawn Johnson
   d) Don Johnson

5. *Semi-Tough*
   a) Dan Jenkins b) Mike Ditka c) Lawrence Taylor
   d) Elizabeth Taylor

6. *The Boys of Summer*
   a) Roger Angell b) Roger Kahn c) Carl Lewis d) Shari Lewis

7. *North Dallas Forty*
   a) Pete Gent b) Troy Aikman c) Emmitt Smith d) Will Smith

8. *Nice Guys Finish Last*
   a) George Steinbrenner b) Leo Durocher c) Billy Martin
   d) Steve Martin

9. *In the Glory of Their Times*
   a) Red Smith b) Grantland Rice c) Lawrence Ritter
   d) John Ritter

10. *Instant Replay*
    a) Jerry Kramer b) Dick Schaap c) Dick Young d) Loretta Young

ANSWERS

1. A.

2. B.

3. B.

4. C.

5. A.

6. B.

7. A.

8. B.

9. C.

10. A.

EXTRA POINT

"Last year wasn't all that bad. We led the league in flu shots."

-*Bill Fitch*, coach of a bad Cleveland Cavaliers team

SAME DAY SCENARIOS

1. Tiger Woods won the U.S. Open June 16, 2002. On the same day in 1975, the L.A. Lakers acquired what big man from the Milwaukee Bucks?

2. On June 8, 2002 Lennox Lewis kayoed Mike Tyson. In 1968 on that day, what pitcher's 58 scoreless inning streak was stopped?

3. On April 8, 1974 Hank Aaron hit homer number 715 to pass Babe Ruth while, in 1975, who became baseball's first black manager?

4. Bob Feller pitched an Opening Day no-hitter April 16, 1940 while, in 1983, what first baseman set the N.L. record for consecutive games played?

5. Paul Hornung was born December 23, 1935. Another running back, on this day in 1972, made the "Immaculate Reception." Name him.

6. Muhammad Ali retired after losing to Trevor Berbick on December 12, 1981. On this day in 1965, who scored an NFL record-tying six touchdowns?

7. On October 3, 1960 Bill Mazeroski hit a walk-off home run to give the Pirates the World Series over the Yankees. Two years later, a football star was born, the NFL's leader in touchdowns. Who is he?

8. The L.A. Lakers completed their three-peat June 12, 2002. What team in, 1991, earned their first NBA championship?

9. Rickey Henderson passed Ty Cobb for the all-time stolen base record May 29, 1990. In 1977, what racing legend won his fourth Indianapolis 500?

10. Barry Bonds hit his 73rd homer October 7, 2001. That very same day, who became the 25th player in major league history to reach 3,000 hits?

ANSWERS

1. Kareem Abdul-Jabbar … He and backup center Walt Wesley went from the Bucks to L.A. for four players.

2. Don Drysdale … It was a record since broken by Orel Hershiser (59 in 1988).

3. Frank Robinson … He managed the Indians to a 5-3 win and punctuated his big day by hitting a home run.

4. San Diego first baseman Steve Garvey played in his 1,118th straight game. He would go on to play a total of 1,207 straight, a record which still stands.

5. Pittsburgh's Franco Harris … He grabbed a deflected Terry Bradshaw pass and scored the winning touchdown in a divisional playoff game between the Steelers and Raiders.

6. Chicago rookie Gale Sayers as the Bears clobbered the 49ers, 61-20.

7. Jerry Rice.

8. The Michael Jordan and Scottie Pippen-led Bulls, over the Lakers 108-101.

9. A.J. Foyt.

10. Rickey Henderson.

MELTING POT

1. What Argentinian-born tennis star won the women's U.S. Open in 1990 and the crown at Wimbledon in 1988 with partner Steffi Graf?

2. Name the Panamanian jockey who won the Kentucky Derby in 1984 aboard Swale.

3. What German won golf's Masters tournament twice?

4. What Cuban-born major leaguer was the first to hit 40 homers and steal 40 bases?

5. Do you know the Munich-born runner who returned there to win a gold medal in the '72 Olympics?

6. Born in Canada, he and his dad are the first father-son duo to win the same NHL trophies: the Lady Byng Memorial and the Hart Memorial. Name him.

7. What Swedish-born tennis player won the U.S. Open back to back in 1991 and '92?

8. This Dutch-born pitcher threw a no-hitter against the California Angels in 1977. Who is he?

9. What Puerto Rican-born second baseman played on the 1992 and '93 Toronto World Series championship teams?

10. Name the East German who won Olympic gold medals in ladies' figure skating in 1984 and '88.

ANSWERS

1. Gabriela Sabatini.

2. Laffit Pincay Jr.

3. Bernhard Langer.

4. Jose Canseco.

5. Frank Shorter, in the marathon … An American, Shorter was born in Germany as his father was a doctor there.

6. Brett Hull.

7. Stefan Edberg.

8. Bert Blyleven.

9. Roberto Alomar.

10. Katarina Witt.

EXTRA POINT

"I wanted to have a career in sports when I was young, but I had to give it up. I'm only six feet tall, so I couldn't play basketball. I'm only 190 pounds so I couldn't play football and I have 20-20 vision so I couldn't be a referee."

-Jay Leno, host of *The Tonight Show*

POTLUCK

1. Who was the first player ever chosen in the NBA lottery?

2. Name the first yacht to win the America's Cup, back in 1851.

3. Who was the first winner of the Byron Nelson Tournament (in 1944)?

4. What's located at 2121 George Halas Drive?

5. What professional sports team has retired the most uniform numbers?

6. Who was the last man to hit a golf ball on the moon?

7. In 1976, he pitched the opening game of the World Series against the New York Yankees. The next year, he pitched the opening game of the fall classic for the Yankees. Name him.

8. What two sporting balls have a maximum allowable weight of 256 ounces?

9. Stonewalling is a term associated with which sport?

10. Of all the golfers to win a major title, who comes first alphabetically?

ANSWERS

1. Patrick Ewing.

2. America. (Ask a simple question and...)

3. Byron Nelson. (Ask another simple question and...)

4. The Pro Football Hall of Fame in Canton, OH.

5. The Boston Celtics, 20.

6. Astronaut Alan Shepard (February 5, 1971).

7. Don Gullett.

8. A bowling ball and a shotput.

9. Cricket.

10. Tommy Aaron, who won the 1973 Masters.

EXTRA POINT

"I'd look for the guy who lost it,
and if he were poor, I'd return it."

-*Yogi Berra*, saying what he would do
if he found $1 million

ON THE AIR

1. What telecast first aired on September 7, 1979 from Bristol, Connecticut with George Grande as its anchor?

2. CBS anchorman Dan Rather got upset and walked off the set when what sporting event ran into his broadcast on September 11, 1987?

3. What CBS/ABC sportscaster was once a Midwest League baseball umpire?

4. Who was the first female play-by-play announcer for a network NFL game?
   a) Gayle Sierens b) Hannah Storm c) Phyllis George
   d) Gorgeous George

5. What New York Giants broadcaster called Bobby Thomson's "shot heard around the world" which gave the club the pennant over the Brooklyn Dodgers in 1951?

6. Name the Super Bowl winning quarterback who was part of the *Monday Night Football* broadcast team in 1985.

7. What Cubs announcer was famous for his seventh inning stretch rendition of *Take Me Out to the Ball Game*?

8. Name the broadcaster who's been doing Dodger games since their Brooklyn days.

9. Who is Vinko Bogataj?

10. What baseball Hall of Famer has been broadcasting New York Mets games since their inception in 1962?

ANSWERS

1. ESPN's *Sportscenter.*

2. The U.S. Open tennis tournament.
   (The CBS screen was blank for six minutes.)

3. Brent Musburger.

4. A ... Sierens made her debut December 27, 1987
   for NBC in a game between the Seahawks and Chiefs.

5. Russ Hodges.

6. Joe Namath.

7. Harry Caray.

8. Vin Scully.

9. He's the skiier seen crashing at the opening of
   ABC's *Wide World of Sports.*

10. Ralph Kiner.

EXTRA POINT

"They should move back first base a step
to eliminate all those close plays."

-John Lowenstein, baseball player

POLITICALLY CORRECT

1. In what year did President Jimmy Carter lead an Olympic boycott to protest the Soviet invasion of Afghanistan?

2. What former pro football quarterback ran for vice-president of the U.S.?

3. Can you name the politico who was a Rhodes Scholar, a College Player of the year, a Final Four MVP and a two-time NBA world champion?

4. What politically incorrect thing did the NFL do on November 24, 1963?

5. What president was captain of his Yale baseball team?

6. Name the president who was the first to have a putting green installed on the White House lawn.

7. Who's the only U.S. senator to pitch a perfect game?

8. Michigan named him their most outstanding football player in 1934. Forty years later he became president of the United States. Name him.

9. In 1995, who became the first congressman to be inducted into the Pro Football Hall of Fame?

10. Who said, "Rail splitting produced an unparalleled president in Abraham Lincoln, but golf hasn't produced even a good A-1 congressman?" a) Mort Sahl b) Jeff Greenfield c) Will Rogers d) Mr. Rogers

ANSWERS

1. 1980.

2. Jack Kemp.

3. Bill Bradley.

4. The league decided not to postpone the scheduled games in spite of the fact that President John F. Kennedy had been assassinated just two days earlier.

5. George Bush.

6. Dwight Eisenhower.

7. Jim Bunning.

8. Gerald Ford.

9. Former Seattle receiver, Steve Largent, a U.S. Representative from Oklahoma.

10. C.

EXTRA POINT

"Mike Anderson's limitations are limitless."

*-**Danny Ozark**, former Phillies manager, on his outfielder's abilities*

FOLLOWING SUIT

Fill in the blank with what suits best.

1. Packers, Packers, Jets, Chiefs, _____

2. Bud Selig, Faye Vincent, Bart Giamatti, Peter Ueberroth, _____

3. Yankees over Dodgers, Yankees over Phillies, Yankees over Giants, Yankees over Dodgers, Yankees over _____

4. The #4 of Earl Weaver by the Orioles, #5 of Brooks Robinson, #20 of Frank Robinson, #22 of Jim Palmer and #33 of _____

5. Assault, Citation, Secretariat, Seattle Slew, _____

6. Ty Cobb, Walter Johnson, Christy Mathewson, Honus Wagner, _____

7. Juwan Howard, Ray Jackson, Jimmy King, Jalen Rose, _____

8. 49ers over Bengals, 49ers over Dolphins, 49ers over Bengals, 49ers over Broncos, 49ers over _____

9. Eddie Collins, Dave Winfield, Lou Brock, Robin Yount, _____

10. George, George, George, George, _____

ANSWERS

1. Colts … This is a list of the first five Super Bowl winners.

2. Bowie Kuhn … These, backtracking, are the last five commissioners of Major League Baseball.

3. Dodgers … These are the teams the Yankees beat in their record-setting string of five straight World Series championships from 1949-'53.

4. Eddie Murray … These are all the retired uniform numbers of the Baltimore Orioles.

5. Affirmed … This is a list of the last five winners of horse racing's Triple Crown.

6. Babe Ruth … These are the five charter members of baseball's Hall of Fame, elected in 1936.

7. Chris Webber … From Michigan, they were known as college basketball's Fab Five.

8. Chargers … In order, these are the teams the 49ers have beaten in the Super Bowl for a perfect 5-0 record.

9. Cal Ripken Jr. … Extra special kudos if you got this one. They are the five big leaguers who have more than 3,000 hits yet never won a batting title.

10. George … If the last one seemed impossible, this was a gimme. They are the names of the five sons of former heavyweight champ George Foreman.

PHRASE CRAZE PHASE 2

Once again, decode these sports items.

1. DLEIF

2. G G
   N E
   I T
   T T
   T I
   E N
   G G

3. BELT
   HITTING

4. 1KNOWS

5. TTTTRRRRRRRRR

6. dribble
   dribble

7. $\dfrac{2}{\text{par}}$

8. issue issue
   issue issue
   issue issue
   issue issue
   issue issue

9. LARETAL

10. PAS

ANSWERS

1. Backfield.

2. Getting up, getting down.

3. Hitting below the belt.

4. Won by a nose.

5. Forty Niners.

6. Double dribble.

7. Two over par.

8. Tennis shoes.

9. Backward lateral.

10. Incomplete pass.

EXTRA POINT

"I don't know. I've never played there."

-Sandy Lyle, golfer, when asked about *Tiger Woods*

SCHOOL DAYS

*Match the following players, all number one NFL draft picks,
with their alma mater.*

1. David Carr   a) Penn State

2. Jeff George   b) Miami

3. Courtney Brown   c) USC

4. Tim Couch   d) Virginia Tech

5. Peyton Manning   e) Kentucky

6. Orlando Pace   f) Tennessee

7. Keyshawn Johnson   g) Washington State

8. Bruce Smith   h) Fresno State

9. Russell Maryland   i) Illinois

10. Drew Bledsoe   j) Ohio State

EXTRA POINT

"I bet on a horse at ten-to-one.
It didn't come in until half-past five."

-*Henny Youngman*, comedian

ANSWERS

1. H.

2. I.

3. A.

4. E.

5. F.

6. J.

7. C.

8. D.

9. B.

10. G.

EXTRA POINT

"No comment."

-*Michael Jordan*, when asked about being named to the NBA's all-interview team

WHO YOU TALKIN' 'BOUT?

Who were the authors of these quotes talking about?

1. "It's a good thing Babe Ruth isn't still here. If he was (he) would have him bat seventh and tell him he's overweight." -Graig Nettles

2. "He speaks English, Spanish, and he's bilingual, too." -Boxing promoter Don King

3. "He's the first guy to drive a $300,000 car with license plates he made himself." -Jay Leno

4. "When _____ goes into a restaurant, he doesn't ask for a menu. He asks for an estimate." -Boxing cornerman Lou Duva

5. "He's so tall that if he fell down, he'd be halfway home." -Darryl Dawkins

6. "Seriously, coach _____ is very fair. He treats us all like dogs." -Henry Jordan

7. "He'd give you the shirt off his back. Of course, he'd call a press conference to announce it." -Catfish Hunter

8. "The definition of an atheist in Alabama is a person who doesn't believe in _____." -Georgia athletic director Wally Butts

9. "Jesus in Nikes." -Former basketballer Jason Williams

10. "That face - it looks like a blocked kick." -Joe Garagiola

ANSWERS

1. George Steinbrenner.

2. Julio Cesar Chavez.

3. Mike Tyson (said after he bought four cars upon his prison release).

4. George Foreman.

5. 7' 6" Manute Bol.

6. Vince Lombardi.

7. Reggie Jackson.

8. Bear Bryant.

9. Michael Jordan.

10. Don Zimmer.

EXTRA POINT

"Absolute silence - that's one thing a sportswriter can quote accurately."

-***Bobby Knight***, basketball coach

"THE" MAN

Identify "the" athletes by their nicknames.

1. The Big Unit

2. The Bald Eagle

3. The Round Mound of Rebound

4. The Pearl

5. The Great One

6. The Commerce Comet

7. The Glove

8. The Mailman

9. The Splendid Splinter

10. The Manassa Mauler

EXTRA POINT

"I don't like the idea of practicing six days to play one."

-**Robin Yount**, baseball Hall of Famer, on football

ANSWERS

1. Randy Johnson.

2. Y.A. Tittle.

3. Charles Barkley.

4. Earl Monroe.

5. Wayne Gretzky.

6. Mickey Mantle.

7. Gary Payton.

8. Karl Malone.

9. Ted Williams.

10. Jack Dempsey.

EXTRA POINT

"Sometimes they write what I say and not what I mean."

-*Pedro Guerrero*, baseball player, on sportswriters

PUCKERING UP

1. True or false? The Montreal Canadiens have won more championships than any team in professional sports history.

2. Just how thick is a hockey puck?

3. Gordie Howe is second to Wayne Gretzky on the NHL's all-time goal-scoring list. With what team did he score his last goal?

4. Speaking of Gretzky, how many career goals did he score?

5. What were Dallas, Phoenix, Calgary and Carolina's previous homes?

6. In 1986, who became the youngest player to ever win the Conn Smythe Trophy?

7. Uniform number one has been retired by five teams- the Rangers, Canadiens, Red Wings, Flyers and Blackhawks. Can you name the players who were so honored?

8. What distinction does Bill Mosienko hold in NHL history?

9. The United States pulled a tremendous upset over the U.S.S.R. in what became known as the Miracle on Ice at the 1980 Olympics. Where were the Games staged that year?

10. What coach has the most all-time NHL victories?

ANSWERS

1. False ... The New York Yankees have won the most titles.

2. One inch.

3. The Hartford Whalers.

4. 894.

5. Minnesota, Winnipeg, Atlanta and Hartford, respectively.

6. Patrick Roy, 20, when he was named playoff MVP with Montreal.

7. Eddie Giacomin, Jacques Plante, Terry Sawchuk, Bernie Parent and Glenn Hall, respectively.

8. He scored the fastest hat trick ever, three goals in 21 seconds for Chicago on March 23, 1952.

9. Lake Placid, New York.

10. Scotty Bowman.

EXTRA POINT

"When he sits down, his ears pop."

-*Don Nelson*, basketball coach, on 7'6" *Shawn Bradley*

LET THE GAMES BEGIN!

1. Who's the only speed-skater to win five gold medals in one single Olympics?

2. How many of the decathlon events can you name?

3. At the 2002 Winter Olympics, after an investigation into the scoring of pairs figure skating, two Canadians were awarded a share of the gold medal with the Russians. Can you name them?

4. When Cassius Clay (later Muhammad Ali) won a gold medal in 1960, in what weight class did he fight?

5. What was the first Olympics in which U.S. pro basketball players competed?

6. When Stella Walsh, who won the gold medal in the 100-meters in 1932, was shot during a robbery attempt, what did an autopsy reveal?

7. Who was attacked by Shane Stant?

8. In his first appearance after winning three gold medals in 1936, Jesse Owens defeated Julio McCaw in a 100-yard race. What was odd about it?

9. What country has won the most gold medals at a single Games?

10. Who preceded Jacques Rogge as head of the International Olympic Committee?

ANSWER

1. Eric Heiden, in 1980.

2. Discus throw, 100-meter dash, 400-meter run, 110-meter hurdles, Pole vault, High jump, Javelin throw, 1500-meter run, Long jump and Shot put.

3. Jamie Sale and David Pelletier … The Russians were Yelena Berezhnaya and Anton Sikharulidze.

4. Light heavyweight.

5. 1992.

6. That she was a he.

7. Nancy Kerrigan, who injured her knee but resumed practice ten days later and wound up with a figure skating silver medal at the '94 Games.

8. Julio was a horse.

9. The United States, 83 gold medals at the Olympic Games in Los Angeles, in 1984.

10. Juan Antonio Samaranch.

INITIALLY SPEAKING- TAKE 2

*Once again, the number on the left is based upon
the first letters for the words on the right.*

1. 0 = N. of W. S. G. in 1994

2. 130 = S.B. by R.H. in 1982

3. 94 = L. of a B. C. (in F.)

4. 38,387 = P. S. by K.A.-J.

5. 2 = O. in a D.P.

6. 7 = G.M. W. by M.S. in 1972

7. 4 = B. in a W.

8. 3 = P. in a H.G.

9. 48 = T. P. by D.M. in 1984

10 660 = H. R. by W.M.

EXTRA POINT

"They broke it to me gently. The manager
came up to me before a game and told me
they didn't allow visitors in the clubhouse."

-***Bob Uecker***, after being told he was cut by a ball club

ANSWERS

1. 0 = Number of World Series Games in 1994

2 130 = Stolen Bases by Rickey Henderson in 1982

3. 94 = Length of a Basketball Court (in Feet)

4. 38,387 = Points Scored by Kareem Abdul-Jabbar

5. 2 = Outs in a Double Play

6. 7 = Gold Medals Won by Mark Spitz in 1972

7. 4 = Balls in a Walk

8. 3 = Periods in a Hockey Game

9. 48 = Touchdown Passes by Dan Marino in 1984

10. 660 = Home Runs by Willie Mays

EXTRA POINT

"You can sum up this sport in two words: You never know."

*-**Lou Duva**, boxing trainer*

HODGEPODGE

1. What award does the Super Bowl MVP receive?

2. Who is the winningest coach in NCAA Division I history?

3. Who was the first non-European to win the Tour de France?

4. Who was the first rookie to make the All-NBA First Team? (Hint: The season was 1979-'80.)

5. What U.S.-based franchise has won the most Stanley Cups?

6. Who was the youngest player to win a home run championship?

7. What Super Bowl-winning team didn't win a game in its first year in the NFL ?

8. In what countries has regular-season major league baseball been played?

9. The "Raging Bull" admitted to a Senate subcommittee that he threw a fight against Billy Fox in 1947. Who is he?

10. What big league baseball stadium was the first to have a retractable roof?

EXTRA POINT

"A good sport has to lose to prove it."

-Anonymous

ANSWERS

1. The Pete Rozelle Trophy.

2. Joe Paterno.

3. Greg LeMond.

4. Larry Bird.

5. The Detroit Red Wings.

6. Tony Conigliaro … He was 20 when he led the AL with 32 homers in 1965.

7. The Dallas Cowboys … They were 0-11-1 in 1960, their first season.

8. The United States, Canada, Mexico and Japan.

9. Jake LaMotta.

10. Toronto's Skydome.

EXTRA POINT

"If it wasn't for golf, I'd probably be a caddy today."

*- **George Archer**, golfer*

TRIVIQUATIONS

Test your math and sports wits here. Fill in the number portion of the answers suggested by the clues and perform the arithmetic to solve it.

Problem #1

1. Take soccer legend Pele's uniform number.

2. Divide that by the number of defeats in Muhammad Ali's career.

3. Multiply that result by the points scored when a safety occurs in football.

4. Take that figure and subract the uniform number of Japanese home run king Sadaharu Oh.

5. The result will yield you the amount of Super Bowl MVP Awards won by Joe Montana.

Problem #2

1. Add the total of Triple Crowns won by Babe Ruth, Willie Mays, and Joe DiMaggio.

2. Divide that by the career number of hits by Roberto Clemente.

3. Subtract the number of intentional walks Roger Maris was given in '61 when he hit '61.

4. Add the uniform number of the first baseball player to have his jersey retired.

5. The sum will be the number of green jackets that Arnold Palmer owns.

ANSWERS

Problem #1

1. 10

2. 10 divided by 5 is 2

3. 2 multiplied by 2 is 4

4. 4 subtracted by 1 =

5. 3.

Problem #2

1. 0

2. 0 divided by 3,000 is 0

3. 0 taken from 0 is 0

4. 4 (Lou Gehrig), so 0 plus 4 =

5. 4.

TENNIS, ANYONE?

1. In the 1992, 1996 and 2000 Olympics, three American women won the gold medal. Can you name them?

2. What's the only Grand Slam tournament Pete Sampras hasn't won?

3. Who participated in the Battle of the Sexes at the Houston Astrodome in 1973?

4. Who's the youngest player to win a Grand Slam singles title?

5. What is officially called "The Lawn Tennis Championships?"

6. What was originally named the International Tennis Challenge Trophy?

7. How wide is a singles tennis court?

8. Of men and women, who has won the most Grand Slam singles titles?

9. Among women tennis players, who's the all-time leading money winner?

10. What man has won the most singles titles?

EXTRA POINT

"I clashed with the drapes."

*-**Jake LaMotta**, boxer, on why his wife left him*

ANSWERS

1. Jennifer Capriati in 1992, Lindsay Davenport in 1996 and Venus Williams in 2000.

2. The French Open.

3. 29-year-old Billie Jean King beat 55-year old Bobby Riggs in straight sets- 6-4, 6-3, 6-3.

4. Martina Hingis, who was 16 years, three months and 26 days old when she captured the Australian Open.

5. Wimbledon.

6. The Davis Cup.

7. 27 feet.

8. Margaret Smith Court, 24 titles.

9. Steffi Graf, $21,895,277.

10. Jimmy Connors, 109.

BROACHING COACHING

1. Who succeeded legendary basketball coach John Wooden at UCLA when he retired after the 1974-'75 season?

2. What is Bill Parcells' first name?

3. In baseball, can a player-manager remove himself from the lineup in the top of the inning and then take over as third base coach in the bottom of the inning?

4. What football coach played right field before Babe Ruth for the New York Yankees?

5. True or false? Ted Giannoulas, in 1969, became the first manager of the San Diego Padres.

6. Who's the last coach to guide his college basketball team to a perfect season? (Hint: They were 32-0 in the 1975-'76 season.)

7. He coached the Vikings to four Super Bowl appearances, Winnipeg to four Grey Cup titles and is the only man in both the Canadian and U.S. Pro Footballs Halls of Fame. Name him.

8. Name the three head coaches with 250 or more NFL wins.

9. Who was the coach of basketball's original Dream Team in 1992?

10. According to NBA rules, is a coach allowed to talk to the referee during a timeout?

ANSWERS

1. Gene Bartow.

2. Duane.

3. Yes.

4. George Halas.

5. False … Preston Gomez was the club's first pilot. Ted Giannoulas is the San Diego Chicken.

6. Indiana's Bobby Knight.

7. Bud Grant.

8. Don Shula, 328; George Halas, 318; and Tom Landry, 250.

9. Chuck Daly.

10. No - only a captain is permitted to do so.

EXTRA POINT

"They wanted an arm and a leg."

-*Martina Navratilova*, when asked why she never insured her left arm

ALL IN THE FAMILY

1. What college basketball player was coached by his father, Press?

2. Name the only brothers to win the Indianapolis 500.

3. The father played for the New York Yankees for 19 years; the son played two seasons with the Bronx Bombers. Who are they?

4. What brotherly duo each has 21 victories to lead the NL in wins in 1979?

5. What brothers have each hit safely in more than 30 consecutive games?

6. Can you name the heavyweight boxing champion whose son was on Super Bowl-winning teams with the Cowboys and 49ers?

7. Name the runner-up at the 1973 Masters whose uncle was a three-time winner of the tournament.

8. On November 14, 1994 Keith and Kerry Cash made NFL history. How?

9. Walter Payton's brother was a running back and kick returner in the NFL for four teams over a five year period. What was his first name?

10. What father-son combination has the most home runs in major league history?

ANSWERS

1. Pete Maravich.

2. The Unser brothers, Bobby and Al.

3. Yogi and Dale Berra.

4. Phil and Joe Niekro.

5. Joe, 56 in 1941, and Dom Dimaggio, 34 in '49.

6. Ken Norton, the 1978 WBC heavyweight champ ...
   His son is linebacker Ken Norton Jr.

7. J.C. Snead ... His uncle, of course, is Slammin'
   Sammy Snead.

8. They became the first twins in the NFL to catch a
   touchdown pass on the same day.

9. Eddie.

10. Bobby and Barry Bonds.

EXTRA POINT

"Crime is down in Miami. They ran out of victims."

-*Pat Williams*, Orlando Magic G.M.

MIXED BAG

1. Of all NCAA Division 1-A coaches with at least 100 victories, who has the best winning percentage?

2. Who has hit into the most double plays in baseball history?

3. Name the four current NBA franchises that were members of the ABA.

4. In the NFL, how many players may a team have on its active roster?

5. Who got fired for punching Charlie Bauman?

6. Can you name the 1977 baseball Rookie of the Year who played his entire 19-year career with one team?

7. Athens is one of three cities which begin with the letter "A" to host the Summer Olympics. Do you know the other two?

8. What prize package stands 13 1/2 inches high, weighs 25 pounds and was designed by New York sculptor Frank Eliscu?

9. Which of pro golf's Majors is the only one played at the same course every year?

10. Who's the only player to lead the big leagues in home runs and E.R.A. (in separate seasons)?

ANSWERS

1. Knute Rockne, 105-12 (with five ties) for an .881 percentage.

2. Cal Ripken Jr., 350.

3. Nets, Nuggets, Pacers and Spurs.

4. 45.

5. Ohio State's coach, Woody Hayes, who was canned the day after he punched the Clemson player near the end of the Buckeyes' 17-15 loss in the Gator Bowl in 1978.

6. Lou Whitaker of the Detroit Tigers.

7. Antwerp (1920) and Amsterdam (1928).

8. The Heisman Trophy.

9. The Masters, at Augusta National Golf Club.

10. Babe Ruth.

EXTRA POINT

"I've had teams before that if you told them to 'go back door,' they left the gym."

*-**Jim Valvano***, basketball coach

I- OPENERS

*These clues all suggest either last names or things
that begin with the letter "I."*

1. In 1972, this man traded his entire team, the Los Angeles Rams, to Carroll Rosenbloom for Rosenbloom's team, the Baltimore Colts.

2. It's where the Dallas Cowboys play their home games.

3. His number 44 has been retired by the Denver Nuggets.

4. He was an All-Big Eight Conference defensive back in 1965 and '66 for the Colorado Buffaloes but became a top performer in another sport - golf.

5. He's the only one in the Baseball Hall of Fame whose last name begins with "I."

6. He coached the Toronto Maple Leafs to their last Stanley Cup championship.

7. On Tuesday, May 30, 1911 Ray Harroun won the inaugural race with a speed of 74.59 miles per hour. What race?

8. They called Lou Gehrig this.

9. He owns the all-time career mark for catches and receiving yardage on the Dallas Cowboys.

10. Brazil's soccer team has been in the last three World Cup finals. Who did they beat in 1994 in a 3-2 shootout after a scoreless game?

ANSWERS

1. Robert Irsay.

2. Irving, Texas.

3. Dan Issel.

4. Hale Irwin.

5. Monte Irvin.

6. Punch Imlach.

7. The Indianapolis 500.

8. Iron Horse of Baseball

9. Michael Irvin.

10. Italy... In 2002, Ronaldo scored two goals as Brazil defeated Germany 2-0 for the World Cup. In 1998 they were shut out by France, 3-0.

LAST CALL

Name the last team each of the following Hall of Famers played on before retiring.

1. Steve Carlton

2. Tony Dorsett

3. Wayne Gretzky

4. Franco Harris

5. Moses Malone

6. Pete Maravich

7. Joe Namath

8. Robin Roberts

9. Warren Spahn

10. Brooks Robinson and Carl Yastrzemski

EXTRA POINT

"There comes a time in every man's life -
and I've had plenty of them."

-*Casey Stengel*, baseball manager

ANSWERS

1. Minnesota Twins.

2. Denver Broncos.

3. New York Rangers.

4. Seattle Seahawks.

5. San Antonio Spurs.

6. Boston Celtics.

7. Los Angeles Rams.

8. Chicago Cubs.

9. San Francisco Giants.

10. The prolific pair are tied for the big league mark for the most years with only one club, 23 - Yaz with the Red Sox and Brooks with the Orioles.

EXTRA POINT

"I can teach things to players, things only I can do."

-*Diego Maradona*, soccer player

BOWL GAMES

*Alright, here's your bonus quiz -
a chance to weigh your bathroom and sports smarts.*

1. The ABA held the first of its kind at the All-Star Game in 1976 which *Sports Illustrated* called "the best halftime invention since the restroom." What is it?

2. "It seems to me the official (baseball) rule book should be called the funny pages. It obviously doesn't mean anything. The rule book is only good for you when you go deer hunting and run out of toilet paper." What manager said this?

3. W.C.- It's the initials for a synonym for bathroom and also the initials for the "father of American football." Name both.

4. Most toilet paper makers manufacture a sheet which is 4 1/2 inches long. In a 1,000 sheet roll, would there be enough paper to go around the perimeter of an NBA court?

5. True or false? When the Rose Bowl first opened it was dubbed the "Bowl without a Bowl" for its scarcity of facilities.

6. "I'm the only coach in history to go straight from the White House to the outhouse." What former Georgia Tech football coach said it?

7. What coach led the Nets to their first ever NBA finals? (Hint: His last name is the same as a leading toilet paper manufacturer.)

8. A simple yes or no will do ... Are there fewer than 50 bathrooms at Kansas City's Arrowhead Stadium?

9. He was the heaviest president ever, so big that he had to have a special bathtub installed in the White House. He was also the first chief exec to throw out an Opening Day ball. Who is he?

10. What was Heisman's (as in the trophy) first name?

ANSWERS

1. Slam Dunk Contest.

2. Billy Martin.

3. Water Closet and Walter Camp.

4. Yes ... 375 feet of toilet paper would be more than ample to cover a court's 288-foot perimeter.

5. False.

6. Pepper Rodgers, who was fired the day after he had lunch with President Jimmy Carter.

7. Byron Scott.

8. Yes - 48. (Nothing's too trivial in this book!)

9. William Howard Taft, in 1910.

10. We hope your mind was in, err, on the toilet here ... The obvious answer is John.